James Rae

40 Modern Studies
in Rhythm and Interpretation

40 moderne Rhythmus
und Interpretationsstudien

for Solo Clarinet
für Klarinette solo

Grades 1 - Diploma

UNIVERSAL EDITION

CONTENTS/INHALT

PREFACE

This book has been written to familiarise the clarinettist with the various rhythms and phrasings encountered in modern music.

Each study deals with a particular aspect of rhythmic playing, ranging from Jazz and Rock to modern Classical interpretation. They are of short to moderate length in order to maximise concentration on style.

The studies have been compiled in order of difficulty to enable the player to gauge his or her progress.

VORWORT

Dieser Band wurde geschrieben, um Klarinettisten mit den verschiedenen Rhythmen und Phrasierungen der modernen Musik vertraut zu machen.

Jede Etüde behandelt einen speziellen Aspekt des rhythmischen Spiels der verschiedensten Stilbereiche, der Jazz und Rockmusik.

Die Etüden sind kurz und nach Schwierigkeitsgraden geordnet. Der Spieler kann sich daher gut auf die einzelnen Stile konzentrieren und seine Fortschritte selbst überprüfen.

James Rae

40 MODERN STUDIES
MODERNE STUDIEN

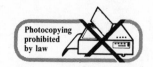
1 Prowlin'

JAMES RAE

2 Undercover

UE 19735L

3 Sad Dance

4 Jumpin'

UE 19735L

4

5 Backtrack

6 In the Wings

7 Slow Motion

UE 19735L

8 The Big One

9 Passing Time

UE 19735L

10 Forever

Medium slow blues tempo

11 Tumbledown Blues

12 In the Beginning

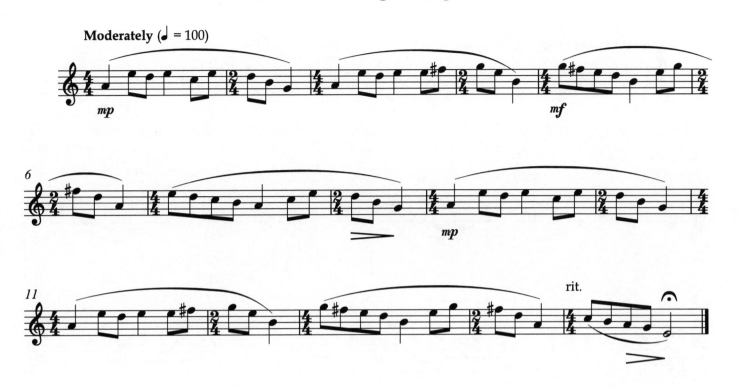

13 Sir Neville

14 Last Chance

UE 19735L

15 Ted's Shuffle

16 Happy Ending

UE 19735L

17 Movin'

Fast swing tempo (♩ = 200) (♫ = ♩³♪)

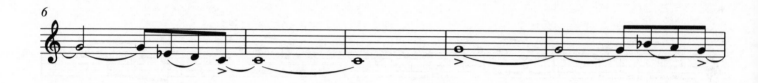

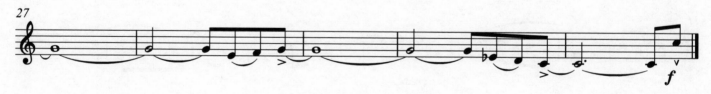

18 Flying Overland

19 Windy Ridge

20 Down to Earth

UE 19735L

21 Catch it!

22 Slavonic Dance

16

23 Dai's Surprise

24 Exclusive

25 Ambiguity

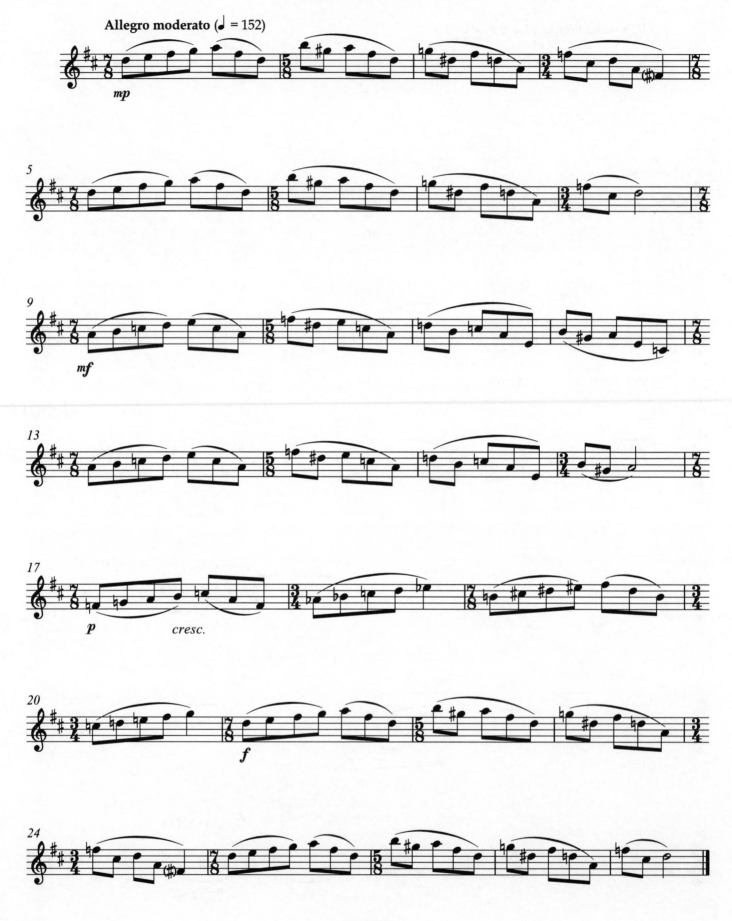

26 On the Brink

UE 19735L

27 Now Hear This!

UE 19735L

28 In a Dream

UE 19735L

29 Helix

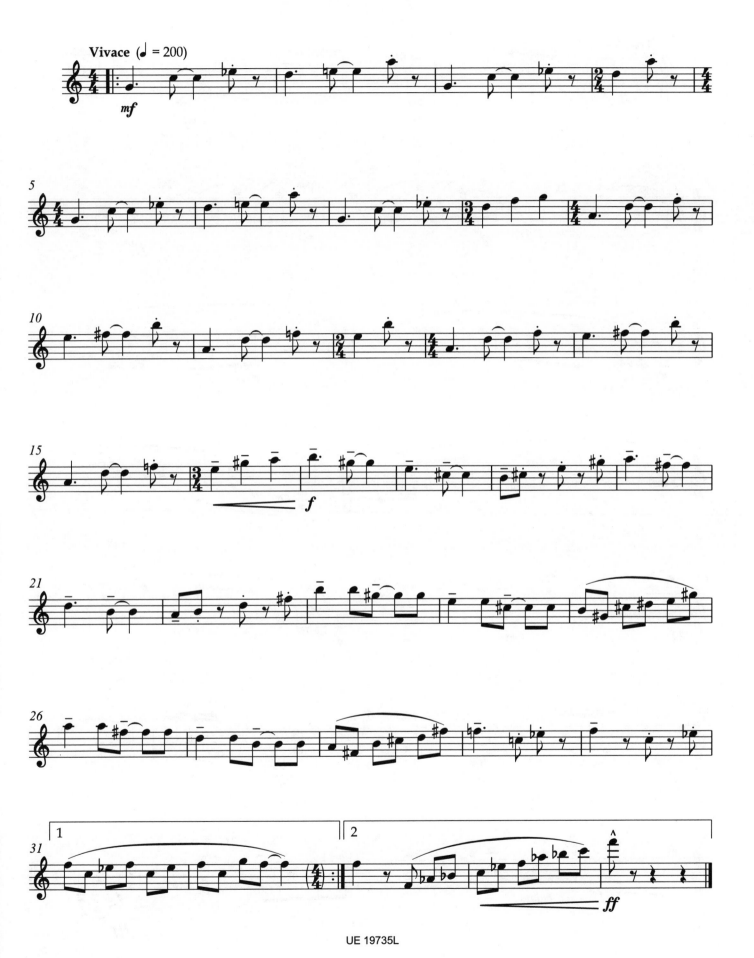

30 All Change!

23

UE 19735L

31 Images

32 Latin Jive

33 Round and Round

34 Entanglement

35 Meditation

36 Hard Rock Blues

UE 19735L

37 Frenzy

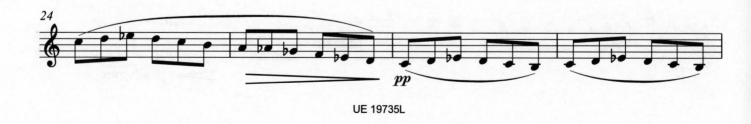

UE 19735L

38 Inside-out

39 Nomad

40 Oiled Wheels

LXI/99

UE 19735L

Reproduced and printed by
Halstan & Co. Ltd., Amersham, Bucks., England

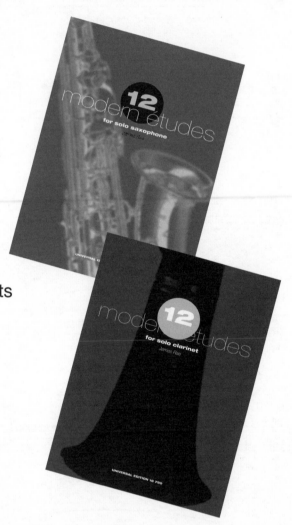